SING SOLO CONTRALTO

——— General Editor: John Carol Case ———

—Edited by Constance Shacklock—

		page
1.	Giordano Caro mio ben	3
2.	Brahms Die Mainacht	6
3.	Delius Twilight Fancies ?	10
4.	Grieg A swan ✓	14
5.	Purcell If music be the food of love	16
6.	Schubert An die Musik ✓	18
7.	Vaughan Williams The water mill ?	21
8.	Handel Return, O God of Hosts ✓	28
9.	Mendelssohn But the Lord is mindful	33
10.	Handel Ombra mai fù	36
11.	Mozart Voi, che sapete	40

3-95

These four volumes are presented with the needs of the younger singer in mind. Each book contains two operatic arias, two oratorio arias, two Lieder or songs in a foreign language, and English songs: a general collection covering a wide variety of periods, but specifically useful to the singer who wishes to gain valuable performing experience at a competitive festival, as a number of classes can be entered with all the necessary music contained in one volume.

Wherever possible Urtext editions, first editions or manuscripts have been consulted, and apart from breath marks which are always editorial, all other editorial markings are either shown in square brackets or as crossed slurs; these are offered as no more than a guide to performance in addition to the composer's own directions. Where further explanation is felt necessary, editorial suggestions are given in a footnote. All German, French and Italian songs are given in their original language together with a singing English translation or paraphrase. In most cases new translations have been specially made. New, simple and stylish piano realisations have been created for all the 'early' songs originally written with continuo accompaniment, and existing piano reductions of songs with orchestral accompaniment have been improved.

I would like to acknowledge the help I have received particularly from Julian Elloway of Oxford University Press, without whose help and guidance these volumes may well have foundered, and from Fiona Floate, his secretary, who coped with much arduous work in the background. I would also like to thank Richard Abrams, René Atkinson, Clifford Bartlett, and Paul Keene, who have provided original texts and in some cases piano accompaniments. But above all, I would like to thank my editorial colleagues Jean Allister, Constance Shacklock, and Robert Tear, with whom, as always, it has been a pleasure to work.

John Carol Case

1. CARO MIO BEN
DEAREST AND BEST

Anon.
Translation by Alan Jones

GIUSEPPE GIORDANI
(1743–1798)

Ca - ro mio ben, cre - di - mi al-
Dear - est and best, heart of my

-men, sen - za di te lan - gui-sce il cor,___
heart, my life is lost if you de - part;___

OXFORD UNIVERSITY PRESS, MUSIC DEPARTMENT, WALTON STREET, OXFORD OX2 6DP

4

1) Suggested ornament: 2) Suggested ornament:

te _____ lan - gui - sce il

2. DIE MAINACHT
THE MAY NIGHT
Op.42 no.2

L. C. H. Hölty
(1748–76)

Translation by John Carol Case

JOHANNES BRAHMS
(1833–1897)

11

wand'l ich trau - rig von Busch zu Busch.
lone - ly, sad - ly I wan - der far.

15

Ü – ber – hül – let vom Laub gir – ret ein Tau – ben-paar
Hid from sight in the trees, songs from a tur – tle dove

18

sein Ent-zü - cken mir vor;
tell of pas - sion-ate love.

21

a – ber ich wen – de mich, su – che dunk – le – re
Ah! Then I turn a – way, hid – ing deep in the

Sing Solo (Contralto)

3. TWILIGHT FANCIES

B. Björnson
(1832–1910)
Translation by F. Copeland

FREDERICK DELIUS
(1862–1934)

Prin - cess look'd forth from her maid - en bow'r. The horn of a herd - boy rang

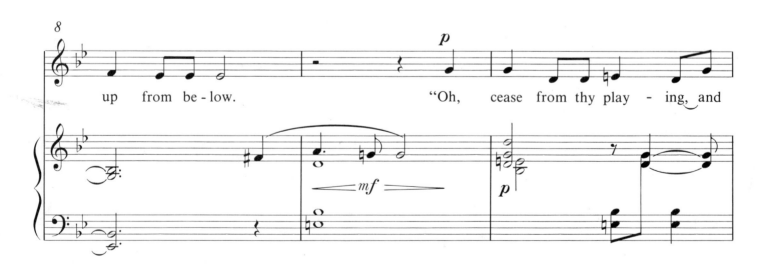

up from be - low. "Oh, cease from thy play - ing, and

haunt me no more, Nor fet - ter my fan - cy that free - ly would soar,"

When the sun goes down, when the sun goes

down. ___ The Prin - cess look'd forth from her

maid - en bow'r, But mute was the horn that had call'd from be - low.

12

4. A SWAN
(1876)

Henrik Ibsen
(1828–1906)
Translation by John Carol Case

EDVARD GRIEG
(1843–1907)

5. IF MUSIC BE THE FOOD OF LOVE
Second setting

H. Heveningham

HENRY PURCELL
(1659–1695)

6. AN DIE MUSIK
TO MUSIC
D 547 (1817)

Franz von Schober
(1798–1882)
Translation by John Carol Case

FRANZ SCHUBERT
(1797–1828)

[cresc.]

Herz___ zu___ war-mer Lieb' ent-zün-den, hast mich in ei-ne___
-spired,___ with___ ar-dent love___ have___ kin-dled, and borne me to a___

cresc.

bess-re Welt ent-rückt, in ei-ne bess-re Welt___ ent-rückt.
bet-ter world of peace, in-to a bet-ter world___ of peace!

p

[pp]

Oft hat ein
Oft has a

fp fp pp

Seuf-zer, dei-ner Harf' ent-flos-sen, ein süs-ser
ca-dence from your harp a-ri-sen, a sweet ca-

20

Sing Solo (Contralto)

7. THE WATER MILL

Fredegond Shove

R. VAUGHAN WILLIAMS
(1872–1958)

take their meat to school, And at dusk they play by the twi - lit

pool; Bare - foot, bare - head, Till the day is

dead, And their mo - ther calls them in to bed._____ The

sup - per stands on the clean-scrubbed board, And the mil - ler drinks like a

8. RETURN, O GOD OF HOSTS
from 'Samson' (1742)

Adapted by N. Hamilton
from John Milton

G. F. HANDEL
(1685–1759)

-turn, re - turn, O__ God__ of Hosts! O God, re-

*Suggested cadenza

be _____ they told.

Sing Solo (Contralto)

9. BUT THE LORD IS MINDFUL
from 'St. Paul'

J. Schubring

FELIX MENDELSSOHN
(1809–1847)

ARIOSO

Andantino ♩ = 66

But the Lord is mind-ful of His own,__ He__ re - mem-bers His chil - -

- dren. But the Lord is mind-ful of His own,__ the Lord re-mem-bers His

chil - dren, re - mem - bers His chil - dren.

Bow down be-fore Him, ye might - y, for the Lord is

10. OMBRA MAI FÙ
Largo from 'Serse'

Adapted from N. Minato
Translation by John Carol Case

G. F. HANDEL
(1685–1759)

giun - ga_a pro - fa - nar - vi au - stro ra - pa - ce.
winds that blow so fierce - ly dare to come near you.

Aria

Larghetto [♩ = 72]

Om -
O_____

11. VOI, CHE SAPETE
TELL ME, FAIR LADIES
from 'The Marriage of Figaro'

Lorenzo da Ponte
(1749–1838)
Translation by E. J. Dent

W. A. MOZART
(1756–1791)

Voi, che sa - pe - te che co - sa è a - mor,
Tell me, fair la - dies, What stirs my heart?

Don - ne, ve - de - te, s'io l'ho nel cor,
You know young Cu - pid, Is this his dart?

Sing Solo (Contralto)

42

Processed and printed by
Halstan & Co. Ltd., Amersham, Bucks., England